NEXUS, T-00:00:00 UTC

1

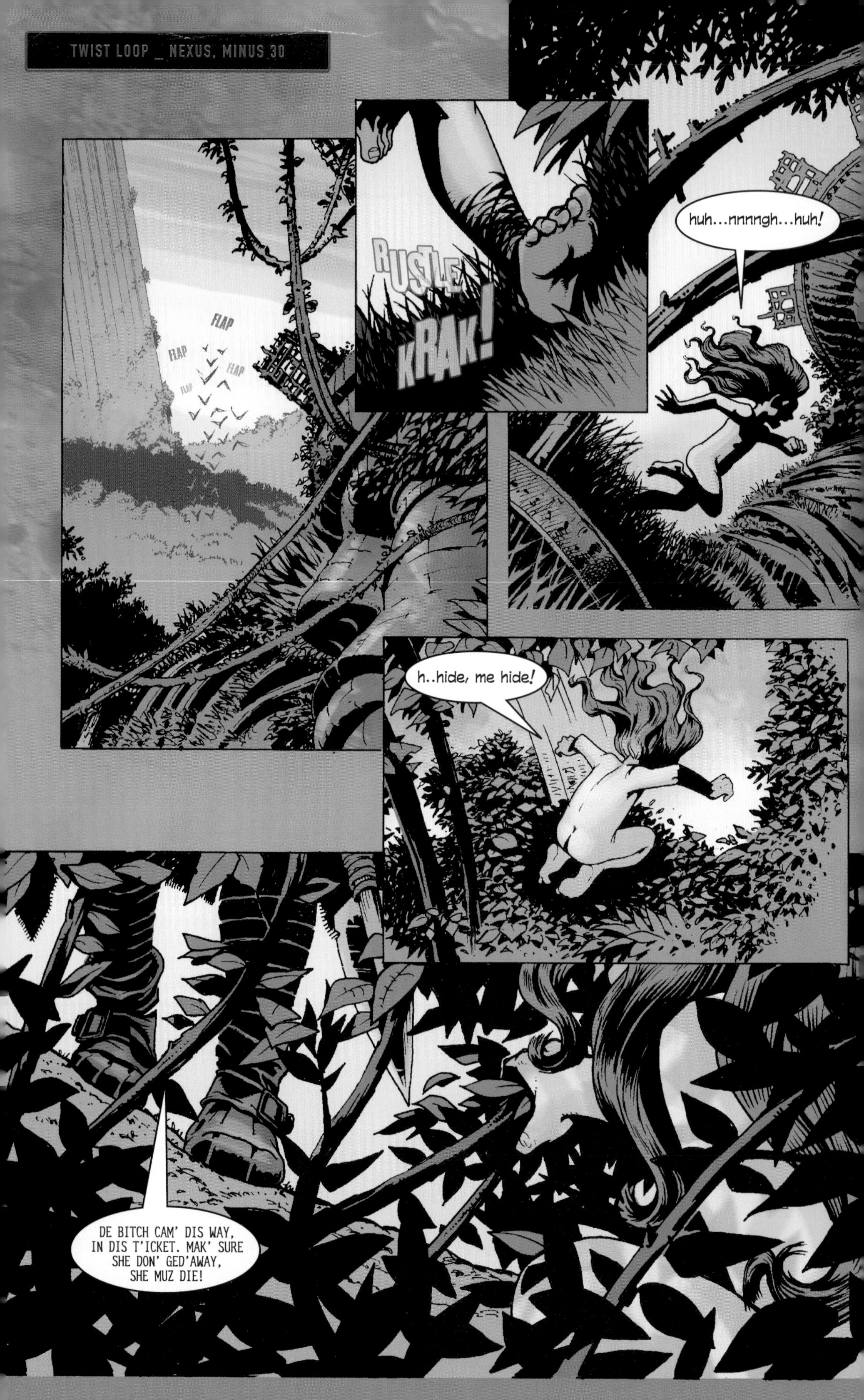

RUSTLE

KRAK!

huh...nnnngh...huh!

FLAP
FLAP
FLAP
FLAP

h..hide, me hide!

DE BITCH CAM' DIS WAY,
IN DIS T'ICKET. MAK' SURE
SHE DON' GED'AWAY,
SHE MUZ DIE!

THEY ARE BENEATH CONTEMPT. GIVE ME THE SISTERHOOD ANYTIME. THEY ARE NOT MEN, THEY ARE SHEEP, THEY DESERVE TO BE CULLED...

rrrrh...

meew?

AT LEAST IT SAVED US A LOT OF TIME WE CAN CONCENTRATE ON FINDING THE LADY.

maamaaah!

PEACE, CHILD.

mmm.......*

I"M NOT SURE I WANT TO, SHE IS VERY POWERFUL. EVEN MISTRESS IS USING THE LADY"S CHILDREN AS HOSTAGES.

TWIST BITCHES. YOU ARE LOOKING FOR ME!

SHIT, LADY HELEN...!

GHAAARGH!

OK, THIS IS THE ADDRESS. KEEP IT TO YOURSELF AND I'LL SEE YOU THERE AT NINE.

GOTCHA! NO TALKING TO STRANGERS; GOT CLEAN UNDERWEAR ON JUST INCASE...

OK, OK. YOU'VE MADE YOUR POINT. JEEZ, IS THERE NO RESPECT FOR YOUR ELDERS NOWADAYS?!

WHAT THE FUCK?

I'LL GO SEE LIEUTENANT BLACK, AND CATCH YOU LATER. AND ROSS, JUST GO CAREFUL, OK?

JUST YOU AN' ME AGAINST THE WORLD. LIKE BATMAN AND ROBIN? CAN'T WAIT TO SEE YOU IN BLACK TIGHTS!

G'WAN, BEAT IT. AND ROSS, DON'T FORGET — "PUT EM DOWN!"

O'MALLEY, WHAT THE HELL.. WHERE'S BLACK?

HE'S BEEN SUSPENDED. ALLEGATIONS HAVE BEEN MADE — TILL THEY HAVE BEEN PROVEN, HE'S OFF ACTIVE DUTIES.

IT'S INNOCENT 'TIL PROVEN GUILTY, O'MALLEY. WHO MADE THE ALLEGATIONS ANYWAY?

YOU KNOW I CAN'T TELL YOU THAT.. AND YOU'RE HERE FOR ONE REASON ONLY, THE *BIN BAG* MURDERS!

THIS STINKS. BLACK, MORE THAN ANYONE, IS THE BACKBONE OF THIS DEPARTMENT.

JEEZUS, FRAME, SHUT THIS CRAP UP. WE HAVE A DEPARTMENT TO RUN, AND 'TIL IT HAS BEEN PROVEN, ONE WAY OR THE OTHER, WE HAVE A JOB TO DO.

LET'S JUST *CONCENTRATE* ON THE 'BIN BAG' MURDERS.

WHY ARE YOU GIVING IT TO ME?

IF I HAD A CHOICE YOU WOULDN'T GET IT! AND IT'S BEEN RUMOURED YOU'RE WORKING ON IT ANYWAY. IF I COULD PROVE IT, I WOULD PUT YOU WHERE BLACK IS!

YOU'RE A LOOSE CANNON, WE DON'T NEED THAT IN THIS DEPARTMENT. BUT SINCE YOU SOLVED 'THE HOOK MURDERS', THE D.A. THINKS YOU'RE A HOTSHOT DETECTIVE. YOU'RE NOT; YOU FLY BY THE SEAT OF YOUR PANTS AND LOSE MORE PARTNERS TO...

CAN IT, O'MALLEY. IT'S ABOUT TIME THIS DEPARTMENT PUT ITS RESOURCES BEHIND THIS CASE.

IT APPEARED NO ONE WAS GOING TO DO ANYTHING ABOUT THESE KIDS GETTING MURDERED. IT SMACKED OF COVER UP.

WHAT IS IT WITH YOU PEOPLE? YOU SEE A CONSPIRACY AROUND EVERY CORNER. JUST DO YOUR JOB AND REPORT EVERYTHING YOU AND YOUR PARTNER DO, TO ME!

I'LL BE FOLLOWING A LEAD AT THE TRANSIENTS' BENEFIT BASH AT THE NEO CLUB TONIGHT. I'LL LET YOU KNOW WHEN I GET A SNIFF.

I DON'T TRUST THAT WARTY BASTARD, ROSS IS WELL OFF OUT OF THE WAY

YEEEEEEEEHHAH!!!

HEADS UP YOU SICK FUCKS, YEEEHA!

BAMM

AAIIEEE!

WHAT THE F...!

ROSS!

SHIT, SHIT, SHIT! THEY HAVE ESCAPED, FOR NOW, BUT I KNOW WHERE TO FIND THEM, AND THERE WILL BE A SACRIFICE! ALL OF YOU, SPLIT UP AND MAKE PREPARATIONS. YOU ALL KNOW WHAT YOU HAVE TO DO. NOW GO!

YOU HAVE ONE CHANCE TO REDEEM YOURSELVES. FRAME IS AT THE NEO CLUB, ERASE HIM AS A PROBLEM. IF NOT— YOU KNOW THE PRICE OF FAILURE!

MR JONES!

YOU HAVE FORTY-FIVE AND COUNTING!

19

A SILENT SCREAM! NOT HEARD ONE OF THEM BEFORE!?

WELL, I DON'T THINK YOU CAN HEAR A SILENT... AHH, YES, VERY FUNNY.

HAVING THE VEIL TORN LIVING, FROM YOUR BODY, IS AS IF ALL THE PAIN FROM YOUR PAST AND FROM YOUR FUTURE IS POURED INTO THIS ONE MOMENT IN TIME

AAH, MY BITCHES, YOU HAVE BROUGHT ME GOOD LADY HELEN.

RAZORJACK, MISTRESS P''AN, IRON QUEEN RULER OF THE TWELVE DIM''S

MY CHILDREN, FREE THEM; I HAVE GIVEN YOU MY BODY FOR THEM; I DID AS YOU ASKED; FOR MY CHILDREN; FREE THEM.

OH HELEN, WHY ARE GOOD PEOPLE SO STUPIDLY TRUSTING? LISTEN MY BITCHES, THIS WEEPING FRAIL IS SSOOO GOOD; GOOD IS BAD, SHE WOULD HEAL YOU. IF YOU WANT TO BE FREE FROM MY TWIST, SHE COULD KILL YOU WITH LOVE!

YOUR CHILDREN HELEN? I HAVE TWISTED THEM, THEY ARE MINE NOW; BUT I CAN GIVE YOU YOUR CHILDREN BACK, AND YOU COULD FREE THEM IF YOU WANT. DO YOU WANT?

NNNNNNNNNNNNOOOOOOOOOOOOOOOOOOOO

THE SQUAD HAS BEEN ACTIVATED MR JONES, THE CLOCK IS RUNNING, WE HAVE THIRTY AND COUNTING.

WE NEED TO FIND HIM OR WE'RE OFF TO HELL IN A HAND CART, MR KAHN.

THEN I THINK WE MAY HAVE A PROBLEM MR JONES.

HE ONLY SAID I LOOK CUTE...

HEY? WHO D'YA THINK YOUR........UMM!

NO WAY CAN YOU TAKE THAT, WITHOUT YOUR EYES WATERING, SEZ I...

YEAH, YOU SHOW ME THAT DUDE, I CAN TAKE HIM, I'M BAD, SOOO BAD!

ANYONE SAY YOU LOOK CUTE, IS ME! YOU DON'T LOOK AT NO ONE ELSE, OR I CUT LOOSE...

DON, YOU SAY WHAT I CAIN'T DO, STOP YOUR MOUTH. AAAAH AH'M HYSTERIAL, AHOWWAH, AHOWWAH, AHOWWAH, AHOWWAH,

WHAT THE ....?

EYE OF NEWT, AND TOE OF FROG, WOOL OF BAT, AND TONGUE OF DOG, ADDER'S FORK, AND BLIND WORM'S STING, LIZARDS LEG....

HEY, COME ON I'M RAVENOUS, LET'S EAT, THE SOUTHERN FRIED'LL GET COLD. AN' YOU'RE STARTING TO LOSE IT.

ITS OK CONTROL, NO PROBLEM. JUST A BUNCH OF KIDS ON THE FLOOR BELOW THE TARGETS.

ALPHA ONE, ANY PROBLEM?

OK. CONCENTRATE ON THE TARGETS. NOW MOVE.

OH, WOW WOODY, THAT WAS SOOO COOL.

I REALLY FELT I WAS AT A MIDNIGHT WITCHES CEREMONY. YOU'RE JUST SO GOOD AT IT, ISN'T HE SIMON ?

MMM....

THANK YOU NATALIE, MS AIMES IN DRAMA SAID I COULD BE THE NEXT CUBA GOODING JR. I FELT I WAS GETTING A HANDLE ON THE CHARACTERS.

HEY, YOU JUST SAID GET A THICK BOOK, THE SUMMER SWIM SUIT SPECIAL WAS THE THICKEST BOOK I COULD GET MY HANDS ON.

I THINK WE WILL BE AT LEAST TWO OF THE BEST WITCHES IN THE "SCOTTISH PLAY" IN THE END OF TERM PRODUCTION. I THINK SIMON IS JUST NOT GETTING INTO IT!

LOOK AT THE PROPS HE GOT...

YES QUITE, SIMON.

DON'T SPILL ANY DRINK ON THE SHEETS. I HAVE TO PUT THEM BACK ON THE BED BEFORE LIGHTS OUT.

DAT IS D'EH MANGIEST CAT, AH EVAH DID SEE!

I THINK HE'S THE KING ALLEYCATS. NO! HE IS THE GOD FATHER OF CATS. HE LIKES PIZZA.

CONTROL, ALPHA TEAM IN POSITION. WAITING FOR THE WORD.

BY PRICKING OF MY THUMBS, SOMETHING WICKED THIS WAY COMES. OPEN LOCKS, WHO EVER KNOCKS.

NOW SIMON YOU SAY, HOW NOW, YOU SECRET, BLACK, AND MIDNIGHT HAGS!

OH WOW. THAT LOOKS SO GOOD.

IT'S ONLY A KETCHUP SACHET!

O'MALLEY! ASSAULT TEAM IN POSITION, WHATS THE WORD?

THE WORD IS......

DEATH IS PLEASURE. TO TAKE SOMEONE AS THEY BREATHE THEIR LAST. TRY IT, FRAME.

MY SOUL WILL NEVER BE BLACK ENOUGH, MR JONES.

APPEASE YOUR BASEST DESIRES. *TAKE ME!*

YOU SICK FUCK!

GOODBYE, FRAME. THE COUNT IS FINISHED. SAY HELLO TO ROSS WHEN YOU MEET HER IN THE AFTERLIFE. I'M WITH MR KAHN — OFF TO HELL IN A HANDCART.

KABOOM

ROSS? *OH SHIT!* THEY KNOW WHERE THEY ARE.

ROSS!

BAM BAM POP BAM PAM

BRRRRRR PAM

TWIST LOOP/CORE LOOP _ NEXUS, MINUS 5

"IS *SHE* DEAD?"

YOU MEAN, YOU *KNEW*???

DON'T WORRY CAPTAIN, YOUR PROMOTION WON'T BE AFFECTED.

PROMOTION? I DON'T GIVE A FLYING FUCK ABOUT PROMOTION, WE HAVE A MAJOR PROBLEM HERE, AND IT'S DOWN TO YOU.

CAPTAIN, SHUT YOUR MOUTH, AN' DO AS YOU'RE TOLD.

PROBLEMS CAN BE BURIED.

...TAKEN TO INQUISITION CRAG, WHERE YOUR FLESH WILL BE STRIPPED FROM YOUR BONES,

YOUR CHILDREN WILL EAT THE OFFAL FROM YOUR ENTRAILS. PREPARE TO DIE, SHE WHO WOULD BE QUEEN!

OH GOD, SIMON WE CAN'T LEAVE HIM...

WE NEED TO GET HELP, THIS CANNOT BE HAPPENING.

HEY! THERE'S SOMETHING IN THERE WITH HIM.

SCREEEECH

ROSS?

CONTROL. BOTH DOWN, STATUS... TARGET MINOR, HEADSHOT, DEAD! TARGET MAJOR... OOH SHIT, SHE'S A COP, THAT'S ROSS!

ALPHA ONE, CAN YOU REPEAT THAT?

WE HAVE JUST TAKEN DOWN A COP! ROSS, DETECTIVE FRAME'S PARTNER!!!

O'MALLEY!!! WE HAVE A MAJOR PROBLEM. IT'S DOWN TO YOU!

TWIST LOOP/CORE LOOP _ NEXUS, MINUS 4

A NEW DIM!? CAN THIS BE? THE POWER, I CAN FEEL IT, CAN IT BE? YESSSS, IT IS THE CORE!!

WE HAVE NO PROBLEM IN THAT BUILDING, CAPTAIN. I AM IN COMPLETE CONTROL!

WOODY!!

THIS CANNOT BE HAPPENING!!

42

FRAME!?

DID YOU REALLY THINK THAT MORON, BLACK, COULD ORGANISE ALL I HAVE PUT IN PLACE? YOU'RE NOT EVEN PART OF THE PLAN!

...DIE FRAME!

...DIE HELEN!

MY BADNESS! WHAT A MAGGOT YOU ARE! IS THIS THE POWER OF THE CORE? NOT THE USUAL SPECIMEN... YOU ARE NOT EVIL. YOU ARE AN INNOCENT. INTRIGUING.

TWIST LOOP _ NEXUS, MINUS 1

A WEAK LINK, BUT YOU SHOULD BE ADEQUATE TO COMPLETE THE NEXUS AND OPEN THE GATEWAY TO THE CORE!

INVITE ME IN! INVITE ME IN, TO LAY WASTE TO YOUR WORLD. TO CREATE A NIGHT THAT WILL LAST A THOUSAND YEARS!!

INVITE MEEEE INNNNNNNNN!!!!

LIEUTENANT, WHAT THE HELL HAPPENED HERE?

A FUCKING DISASTER, WHAT THE FUCK DO YA THINK?!!

SORRY LIEUTENANT, HE'S NOT GONNA MAKE IT.

NOT ANY MORE. WHAT HAPPENED?

WE THINK IT WAS A GAS EXPLOSION.

O'MALLEY HAD ORGANISED A SWAT OPERATION; IT WAS A FUCK-UP. WE MANAGED TO HIT AN UNDERCOVER OP, RUN BY DETECTIVE FRAME. HIS PARTNER, ROSS, HAS BEEN SHOT BY THE SWAT TEAM.

SHIT!!! NOW WHO THE FUCK WANTS TO... CAPTAIN BLACK! I THOUGHT YOU WERE SUSPENDED?

WHERE'S O'MALLEY NOW?

HE'S IN THE CITADEL WITH FRAME AND ROSS!

WE HAVE TO GET INTO THE CITADEL.

SORRY CAPTAIN, THIS IS WHAT THE EXPLOSION DID! WE HAVE THE NATIONAL GUARD BUILDING TRANSIT BRIDGES, BUT IT WILL TAKE AT LEAST AN HOUR.

47

BANG!

HEY OTIS! HOW YA HANGIN'? GONNA BE LONG?

NAH! JUST GOTTA WEIGH THIS THEN BE RIGHT WITH YA. WHAD'YA GOT?

SHHEESH! DON'T BELIEVE IT. IT'S THAT COP, FRAME. NEVER THOUGHT I'D LIVE TO SEE HIM IN HERE.

YEAH, HE'S PUT MORE PEOPLE IN HERE THAN ANY OTHER ONE COP. STRANGE STORY; I'LL TELL YA OVER COFFEE.

HURH! JUST COVER HIM, HIS EYES ARE WEIRD!

IF YOU'RE BUYIN', I'LL HAVE A CHEESEBURGER, RARE, TO GO WITH IT.

DON'T KNOW HOW YOU CAN EAT AFTER WHAT YOU'VE HAD YOUR HANDS IN!

NOKK NOKK!!!

GO AWAY!!!

OH, CAPTAIN BLACK. I THOUGHT IT WAS THE PRESS AGAIN.

AH ROSS, YES, I HEARD. WE HAVE POSTED A GUARD TO STOP THEM GETTING TO YOU.

IT'S BEEN SIX WEEKS SINCE, YOU'D THINK THEY'D HAVE OTHER THINGS TO PUT IN THEIR PAPERS FOR A SENSATIONAL FIX FOR THE MASSES OVER BREAKFAST.

YOU'VE HAD VISITORS I SEE.

YEP, THE GUYS FROM THE DEPARTMENT HAVE BEEN IN. I THINK THEY'RE TRYING TO GIVE ME A CASE OF TERMINAL HAY-FEVER WITH ALL THE FLOWERS!

WHAT IS THE CITY LIKE NOW?

BAD. IT'S FALLING APART. RIOTS ARE BREAKING OUT SPORADICALLY.

HAVE YOU FOUND HIM YET?

NO. I'M SORRY.

WE STILL DON'T UNDERSTAND. HE WAS CERTIFIED DEAD AT THE CITADEL. HOW HE GOT UP AND WALKED FROM THE MORGUE WE HAVE NO IDEA.

HEY ROSS, LOOKIN' GOOD!

HEY SIMON, WHERE HAVE YOU BEEN FOR OUR CHESS GAME THESE LAST COUPLE OF WEEKS?

YOUR GUARDS WOULDN'T LET ME IN.

AH RIGHT, SORRY ABOUT THAT.

AND NAT?

SHE'S BEEN IN EVERYDAY. SHE ALWAYS HAD A THING FOR WOODY – HE WAS THE COOL GUY IN COLLEGE! ALWAYS THOUGHT HE WAS A PRICK M'SELF.

WOODY'S JUST NOT RESPONDING. THE DOCS THINK IT'S ALL IN HIS MIND.

SHE WEARS MY RING AROUND HER NECK, HAS DONE SINCE WE WERE SIXTEEN. SHE IS STILL MY GIRL... I THINK.

LET ME BUY YOU A COKE. HERE IS MY CARD, ANYTIME YOU NEED TO TALK, GIVE ME A CALL.

NOKK. NOKK!

THIS HAD BETTER BE IMPORTANT!

ROSS, GOOD TO HAVE YOU BACK ON ACTIVE DUTY.

I NEED TO BE BUSY. THANKS FOR THE PROMOTION.

NO WORRIES. YOU DESERVE IT. O'MALLEY'S DEAD, WE'VE PUT HALF THE CITY COUNCIL AND THE POLICE DEPARTMENT AWAY FOR LIFE. WE NEED YOU.

WE HAVE TO FIND OUT WHAT HAPPENED TO THOSE KIDS. THE POLICE PSYCHIATRISTS THINK IT WAS GROUP HYSTERIA. BUT THAT DOESN'T EXPLAIN WOODY.

THE CITY IS STILL SHAKIN' APART AT THE SEAMS. BUT WITH YOU BACK, WE AT LEAST HAVE SOME EXPERIENCE IN THE DEPARTMENT AT THE SHARP END. WELCOME BACK.

THE CITADEL IS STILL SURROUNDED BY THAT CHASM. GOD KNOWS WHAT CAUSED IT. NOT GAS FOR SURE.

SIMON, HOW'S IT GOIN?

NOT GOOD. JUST COMIN' ROUND TO TALK.

WOODY DISCHARGED HIMSELF FROM THE HOSPITAL AND NAT IS ALWAYS AROUND THIS SLUM HE'S LIVIN' IN.

LOOK, I HAVEN'T GOT TIME JUST NOW, BUT GIVE ME A CALL LATER AND WE WILL MEET UP.

SURE, THANKS ROSS.

IS IT A "KILLER SMILE" VICTIM?

CAPTAIN BLACK! YES, THE SEVENTH ONE. IT HAS ALL THE USUAL SIGNS, AND A COUPLE OF NEW TWISTS WHICH WE CAN'T EXPLAIN.

THE SAME CARVING OF THE FACE INTO THE "KILLER SMILE".

AMPUTATED THE HANDS.

THIS IS NEW— HE RIPPED OUT THE VICTIM'S EARRINGS.

DISEMBOWELLED THE BODY.

THE NAILING OF THE EVISCERATED INTESTINES WITHIN A PENTANGLE, THE HAND NAILED IN THE MIDDLE.

WHAT WE CAN'T EXPLAIN, IS THE DOOR WITHIN THE PENTANGLE, THERE IS NO DOOR AT THIS POINT IN THE BUILDING PLANS.

I WANT TO LOOK AROUND THE SCENE A BIT LONGER.

FINE. KEEP ME POSTED.

HOLD STILL FRAME, FIRST THE FACE, THEN...

ARRGHH!

HUOOM!!

I THINK IT IS TIME TO STEP BACK THROUGH THE DOOR MR KAHN. I TAKE YOUR SILENCE FOR ASSENT.

MR JONES, MR KAHN, LET ME RELEASE YOU...!!

AND THAT WAS THE LAST IMAGE ON THE TAPE.

THIP

YOU SAY THE ORDERLIES WENT TO THE CELL AND FOUND NOTHING! NO BLOOD; NO FRAME? NOTHING?

THEY SAID,"ONLY THE ECHO OF SCREAMS!!!" I DIDN'T THINK MEDICS HAD THAT MUCH IMAGINATION.

THAT THING, THAT WASN'T FRAME; ALMOST, BUT DEFINITELY NOT THE FRAME I KNEW. AND MR KAHN WITH NO FACE, THAT IS NOT POSSIBLE.

ROSS, SOMEONE TO SEE YOU!

AFTER SEEING THIS TAPE, I THINK ANYTHING IS POSSIBLE.

WHAT THE HELL **WAS** THAT THING? AND YOU? YOU'RE NOT FRAME ANYMORE!

SHE SAVED ME, SAVED US ALL.

WHAT OF NAT AND POOR WOODY?

I AM, ROSS, I AM FRAME AND MORE: WHEN I 'DIED' SOMEHOW HELEN JOINED WITH ME.

SOMEHOW, WOODY HAD THE STRENGTH OF WILL NOT TO KILL NATALIE. IF HE HAD, HE WOULD HAVE OPENED A DOORWAY TO LET THAT CREATURE, RAZORJACK, INTO OUR WORLD. ALL OUR WORST NIGHTMARES WOULD HAVE COME TRUE.

WELL, WE BEAT HER NO PROBLEM WITH "YOUR FRIEND!"

RAZORJACK WILL BE BACK ROSS, SOMEHOW. BUT FOR NOW LET'S HELP GET THE CITY BACK TO NORMAL.

WHAT ABOUT YOUR HOUSE GUEST? IS SHE... FOREVER!?

I THINK SO. WE BOTH HAVE A LOT TO LEARN ABOUT EACH OTHER, TO FIND OUT WHAT WE HAVE BECOME.

WE ONLY BEAT RAZORJACK BECAUSE IT DIDN'T KNOW HELEN WAS INSIDE ME, AND IT HADN'T FULLY-CROSSED OVER. WOODY DIED WHEN I, WHEN **HELEN** HEALED HIM TO RID HIM OF RAZORJACK.

WELL, SHE'S DEFEATED NOW, THANKS TO YOU... ER, TWO!?

THE FIRST THING I HAVE TO TEACH HER IS... HOW TO STAND AND PEE!!!!

THE END

DEAD FALL

or

FURTHER TALES OF THE TRANS-DIMENSIONAL DETECTIVE, HIS SIDEKICK
AND THE BIG BLACK HOUSE FULL OF DOORS.

SHLURP

THANKS, ROSS.

YOU GOTTA PUT 'EM DOWN FRAME, REMEMBER?

WHERE DID YOU END UP THIS TIME?

P'TSUNU THE WATER PLANET!

GOTTA DO MORE TO STOP THIS EVIL BITCH, FRAME. BEFORE ANOTHER INNOCENT DIES BY OUR HAND!

HELP ME...

WE'RE GONNA HAVE TO TAKE IT TO HER ROSS!

THE END?

I enjoy doing fully-painted covers, I find doing the detailed graphite pencils over which I paint very liberating after drawing for line. I enjoyed giving expression to creatures that only exist in my imagination, and the twist bitches have become characters I would like to explore in more detail in future projects.

This was the first appearance of Razorjack on the cover for the Razorjack magazine produced for Jack Publishing. I had no real idea what she was going to look like when I started to draw her, she evolved just to fit the cover as she was not going to appear in the first story arc. I was rather pleased with the way she turned out. The cover idea was to show Razorjack as an evil presence, who was controlling events but was invisible to the people she was manipulating, so she goes unnoticed as the S.W.A.T. team are sweeping through her to control a situation of her making.

This was the cover for the second book from Com X, here I wanted to depict Lady Helen as a tortured soul trapped between dimensions after she was killed by Razorjack. It was a mixture of painting and Photoshop manipulation.

Ah, Ross. The first portrait of Frame's sidekick done for this collected edition. Behind her and always in her and Frame's shadow is the constant presence of Razorjack and her minions (always wanted to use that word) the Twist Bitches who are constantly clawing and screaming to break down the thin skin between our reality and their nightmare.

I want to say a thank you here to all my cover models, Una, Jenna and Suvd.

To depict Razorjack in line, to have her work in three hundred and sixty degrees was a major problem, but by the end of the first issue I felt I was starting to know her, and she became more fluid and more fun for me to draw.

To have so little time to design all of the characters can create time constraints which actually help the creative process as you have to simplify, which can make a more effective costume. The Twist Bitches, in skintight leather, was a design chore I could happily have endured all week long. I don't know why!

This page

I was surprised how many variations I kept uncovering of Razorjack when cleaning out the studio. This was lifted from the cover pencils for the Jack publication of Razorjack, for limited edition prints I did for that first venture into self-publishing. I just thank Mac for computers; they can make publishing life a lot easier.

Opposite page

Here, I used the pencil image (again) from the first cover of Razorjack to do her in line with some design tweaking so she could stand alone. Not too bad but a bit stiff, I still needed to get to know her better.

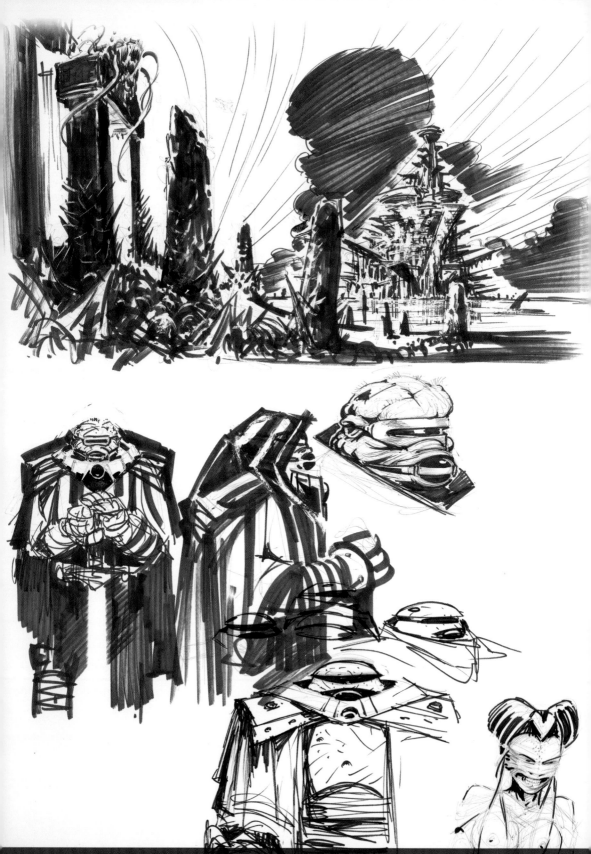

To start to get a feel for the world I am creating, I doodle around scenes for as long as the deadline allows, sometimes an image will appear that I can use in the story, more often than not, it is just something that gives depth to the world, and an idea for an image that no one will ever see.

Below Left

This was the first attempt to do Razorjack within the story line you have in your hands. I just was not happy with it. When I started drawing her I wanted her to appear evil, which I felt she was in this interpretation, but graphically it was not a satisfying image.

Above Right

This is the Razorjack that I ended up using in that panel in the story, but it was only toward the end of the first issue I really felt happy with the way she started to appear in line.

Below Left

The first appearance of Mr J and Mr K, in *that* Jack publication again, (who *is* this Jack?). I have a major soft spot for them. A number of people have said how much they liked them; considering they're psychos, that's nice! Mr J and Mr K, after Ross, were the ones who became more real for me than any of the other characters.

Above Right

And here they appear for the first time in this story line. Polite killers are a chilling concept; they have appeared in all forms of story telling, and one of my favorite scenes where it is played to perfection, is in the Marathon man, by that fine old thespian Laurence Olivier. I still look at distinguished white haired old gentlemen with suspicion because of that movie, and dentists.

Above

This is the very first page of visualizing art I did for my self published Razorjack. The page that started me off on this saga such an age ago... people have been born and died since I started this venture and I, I would like to be profound here but... I can't be arsed. I over manipulated it in Photoshop and lost a lot of detail but it gave me a direction for the first Razorjack cover. Just thought you would like to see it.

Right

Here a two examples of the cover from the first publication of Razorjack. Can you spot the difference? Yes, one has the lettering on. Anything else? A nudie on a cover!! I wonder if I really thought I would get away with it!? The distributors suggested if I wanted that cover on show, it needed to be clothed. I don't think it bothered me that much having to clothe her, but having seen some of the costumed girly covers for some comics (and I am a fan of them when they are done well) mine seemed quite tame in comparison. Finally, if I haven't said "great job" to the designer of this series I do now — stand and take a bow Eddie, thanks again for such a top quality design job and still being here as Com X and still being my mate.

Additional thanks to Sally Hurst for exemplary work in my studio for the last three years and for the new colour work on this edition of Razorjack, and for Craig Johnson, a believer who ran his eyes over the script for me and tightened up the loose bits, any mistakes and bad grammar is mine and not his.